HEATHCLIFF
DOG DAYS

The funniest feline in America delights millions of fans every day as he appears in over 1000 newspapers. You'll have a laugh a minute as Heathcliff tangles with the milkman, the cat show judge, the veterinarian, and just about everyone else he runs into. If you're looking for some fun, look no further. Heathcliff is here!

Heathcliff Books

HEATHCLIFF
HEATHCLIFF RIDES AGAIN
HEATHCLIFF TRIPLE THREAT
HEATHCLIFF WANTED
HEATHCLIFF SPINS A YARN
HEATHCLIFF DOES IT AGAIN!
HEATHCLIFF STRIKES AGAIN!
HEATHCLIFF ROUND 3
HEATHCLIFF PIGS OUT
HEATHCLIFF FIRST PRIZE!
HEATHCLIFF'S TREASURE CHEST OF PUZZLES
HEATHCLIFF'S PUZZLERS
HEATHCLIFF PUZZLE SLEUTH
HEATHCLIFF BANQUET
HEATHCLIFF FEAST
SWEET SAVAGE HEATHCLIFF
WICKED LOVING HEATHCLIFF
HEATHCLIFF IN CONCERT
HEATHCLIFF PLAY BY PLAY
HEATHCLIFF DINES OUT
HEATHCLIFF GONE FISHIN'
HEATHCLIFF CLEANS HOUSE
HEATHCLIFF WORKING OUT
HEATHCLIFF CATCH OF THE DAY
HEATHCLIFF ON VACATION
HEATHCLIFF KOOL KAT
HEATHCLIFF ROCKIN' AND ROLLIN'
HEATHCLIFF SMOOTH SAILING
HEATHCLIFF ALL AMERICAN
HEATHCLIFF TOP SECRET
HEATHCLIFF CHAIRMAN OF THE BOARD
HEATHCLIFF DOG DAYS

HEATHCLIFF®
DOG DAYS

by Geo Gately

J

JOVE BOOKS, NEW YORK

Originally included in the Charter Books
collection *Heathcliff Play By Play.*

HEATHCLIFF DOG DAYS

A Jove Book / published by arrangement with
McNaught Syndicate, Inc.

PRINTING HISTORY
Jove edition / April 1988

ISBN: 0-515-09591-5

Jove Books are published by The Berkley Publishing Group,
200 Madison Avenue, New York, New York 10016.
The name "JOVE" and the "J" logo
are trademarks belonging to Jove Publications, Inc.

PRINTED IN THE UNITED STATES OF AMERICA

10   9   8   7   6   5   4   3

"HE'S CLEANING OUT
THE ATTIC."

"EIGHT BALL...

...IN THE CORNER POCKET."

" NOW, HEAR THIS!..."

"HE LOVES THE CAR HOPS!"

"KEEP THAT LID ON OR YOU WON'T HAVE ANY MICE LEFT!"

"WHERE WERE YOU ON THE NIGHT OF JANUARY 24TH?!"

"MY GOSH!..HOW MANY FIGHTS HAS HE BEEN IN TODAY?!"

"FIVE."

"I'M NOT INTERESTED IN THE DANG CAT FOOD COMMERCIALS!"

"OFF ON A SKIING TRIP?"

"PRETTY KITTY'S AHEAD BY A LENGTH!"

"I'D BETTER GET HOME...WHERE'S MY HAT AND COAT?"

"THAT'S NOT EXACTLY HOW IT WORKS."

1982
McNaught Synd., Inc

"YOU ARE NEVER, EVER TO APPEAR AT *'SHOW AND TELL'* AGAIN!"

"WILL YOU JUST BRING ME THE PAPER?!!"

"OH, NO!.. NOT GRANDMA'S NEW BALL OF YARN!"

"I'M AFRAID I MUST DISTURB YOU."

"HE HAD A MANICURE WHILE YOU WERE
UNDER THE HOT TOWEL."

"WE HAVE A FEW COMPLAINTS
ABOUT OUR CAT FOOD..."

"ALMOST FORGOT!...IT'S MY BOWLING NIGHT!"

"WILL YOU GO HOME?!!"

"PUNCHING OUT?"

"MY GOSH! LOOK AT THAT!!"

"IT'S ALMOST OVER ... THEY'RE INTO
THE SPIN CYCLE."

"NO...THERE MUST BE
ANOTHER WAY."

"CONFOUNDED CHILD-
PROOF CAPS!"

"BATTEN DOWN THE HATCHES!"

"SORRY...HE MISTOOK YOU FOR A POODLE."

"GO ON....I'M LISTENING."

"AT THE RISK OF SEEMING INHOSPITABLE..."

" RELAX ..... ACT NONCHALANT. "

"LOST HIM!"

"SORRY ABOUT THAT!"

"THE 'HUNK' IS HERE."

1982
McNaught Synd. Inc

"JUST THE BALL...LEAVE THE BIRD!"

"I THINK HE'S LEAVING HOME AGAIN."

"YOU'LL SEE!"

"HE DOESN'T
LIKE CHICKEN."

1982
McNaught Synd. Inc.

"WELL!....IF IT ISN'T THE EASTER BUNNY!"

"HERE COMES CRAZY SHIRLEY
UNDER THE MISTLETOE!"

"HE'S BEEN GONE FOR DAYS THIS TIME!"

"YOU BETTER QUIT FEEDING HIM PEANUTS!"

"WELL, YOU'LL JUST HAVE TO HOLD THE
'MISS HEATHCLIFF PAGEANT' ELSEWHERE."

"DON'T BET IT..I GOTTA TAKE A DIVE."

"I TOLD YOU NOT TO BRING POPCORN!"

"OH, GOOD, YOU FOUND MY PET ALLIGATOR."

"NEVER MIND PUTTING A CANDLE IN THE WINDOW!"

"WHILE YOU WERE DOZING...."

"WILL YOU FORGET THE FISHING ?!"

"...IN RESPONSE, THE WITNESS REPLIED, 'ROWRR, SPIT, RIP, SHRED, REND'."

"WE MANAGED TO SCARE AWAY THOSE NASTY HICCUPS!"

"HE DIDN'T HAVE HICCUPS."

"NO, BUT I DID!"

 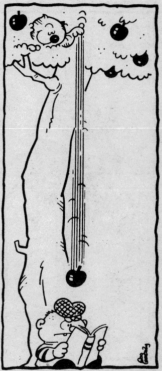

"I DON'T UNDERSTAND THIS THEORY OF GRAVITY STUFF!"

"MOVE ALONG, WISE GUY!"

"I'LL CHOOSE THE GIFTS!"

"THIS IS THE LAST TIME I TAKE YOU
DUCK HUNTING!"

"SONJA GETS ANGRY WHEN CRAZY SHIRLEY CHASES HEATHCLIFF."

"SHH..I'M WATCHING MY FAVORITE SOAP OPERA."

"SO AM I."

"JUST SLIP HIM A MINNOW AND HE GOES AWAY."

"IT'S SONJA."

"SPIKE IS ON 'HOLD'."

"I THINK WE'VE SEEN ENOUGH OF 'HOW HEATHCLIFF SPENT HIS SUMMER VACATION'!"

" THIS ONE'S IN THE ARM. "

"I SEE WE'RE COLLECTING DRIFTWOOD!"

1982
McNaught Synd., Inc

"I NEVER HEARD OF A SEASON PASS
TO THE AQUARIUM!"

" WE DON'T ACCEPT CREDIT CARDS. "

"MARCH YOURSELF RIGHT OUT OF HERE
AND TAKE YOUR SIGN WITH YOU!"

"THAT DOES IT!.. NO MORE BUNK BEDS,
AND NO MORE STRAYS!"

"YOU'RE ALLOWED ONE PHONE CALL."

"QUICK, SHOPPERS!..IF YOU'LL RACE
TO THE PET FOOD SECTION..."

"I'M AFRAID YOU'D HARDLY QUALIFY AS OUR POSTER BOY."

"IT'S HIS FAVORITE CORNER."

"WELL, WE'VE GOT AN IMPRESSIVE CROP OF ROOKIES...."

"CAN YOU WAIT 'TIL I GET DRESSED
AND INTO MY CHAIR?"

"SORRY TO KEEP YOU WAITING!"

"THIS WAY I'LL KNOW WHAT MISCHIEF
YOU'RE INTO!"

DING·A·LING

"THIS CALLS FOR SURGERY...WE HAVE TO REMOVE THE BIRD BATH."

"WE DON'T HAVE SALMON."

"NO STEAK FOR PUSSYCATS."

"SCRAM, PEST!"

"HE'S DOUBLE PARKED."

"...AND ANOTHER THING ABOUT YOUR
SMART-ALEC CAT..."

"ANOTHER BIG NIGHT ON THE TOWN?"

"THIS IS OUR PIT STOP."

"C'MON, FATSO,
GIMME A TURN
ON THE SWING!"

" I *KNOW* WHICH FOOT IT GOES ON !"

"HE LOVES TO PLAY!"

"GET OUTA HERE!"

"I'LL HANDLE THE DUAL CONTROLS!"

"IT'S BAGGY PANTS
COMEDY NIGHT."

"LOOK OUT FOR A BUNT!"

"CRAZY SHIRLEY STEAMED OPEN THE MAIL!"

" I WISH YOU WOULDN'T OPEN YOUR GIFTS LIKE THAT!"

"THE ACCUSED WAS STANDING APPROXIMATELY HERE."

"THAT'S ENOUGH SHOPPING FOR TODAY."

"WE FORGOT CAT FOOD!"

"'YES,' IT'S MY BOWLING NIGHT, AND 'NO,'
I DON'T WANT COMPANY!"

" FAT CHANCE ! "

"WHEN THE CAT SWATS THE CUCKOO,
IT'LL BE 1982!"

"HE LIKES TO CHECK FOR CAT FOOD COUPONS."

"WELL, THE HORN WORKS."

"HE'LL PROBABLY OBJECT TO OUR HOT TUB!"

"AWRIGHT... I'LL SING IT ONE MORE TIME...
'♪ ON THE ROAD AGAIN...♫...'"

"CANCEL THAT INSPIRATION!"

"WELL!... GOOD MORNING, PENGUINS!"

"WE'LL DISCUSS IT NO FURTHER!"

"WILL YOU KNOCK OFF THAT RAIN DANCE?!"

"NOW CUT THAT OUT!"

"NO RIDERS!"

"GET DOWN HERE!"

"THAT'S TOPS ON HIS LIST....
A DESIGNER SCRATCHING POST!"

"SMOKING SECTION ?...OR NON SMOKING ?"

"THAT STANDS FOR CATNIP...STRICTLY OFF LIMITS!"

"HERE COMES WEALTHY UNCLE AVERY.
BOY!.. HE'S GOT A GOOD OLD SOCK!"

"HOW THOUGHTFUL!... A CANDY CANE!"